THE BULLET-POINT LIFE PLANNER

GET ORGANIZED, PLAN YOUR LIFE, TRACK YOUR HABITS, AND BRAINSTORM FOR THE FUTURE

WENDY HOBSON

ARCTURUS

ARCTURUS

This edition published in 2018 by Arcturus Publishing Limited
26/27 Bickels Yard, 151–153 Bermondsey Street,
London SE1 3HA

ISBN: 978-1-78828-007-5
AD005820UK

Printed in China

WELCOME TO YOUR BULLET-POINT LIFE PLANNER

I tried very hard to get used to using a calendar on my phone but it was somehow just too clinical, too neat and tidy – like a house where you're too scared to sit down for fear of squashing the beautifully plumped pillows. I loved the fact that you could put an event in once and repeat it (Pilates every Monday at 7.30) until the cows come home but I never managed to combine it successfully with my to-do list. It was never a comfortable fit.

There is just something about using a notebook and pen that allows you to create a visual picture of what's going on in your life. You can use colour to group things together, write in different directions on the page and in different sizes, circle blocks of text and link them together, doodle round them, underline them, cross them out, highlight them. It's organic. It's creative. And it's hugely satisfying.

So I went back to my trusty pen and paper and looked at what I was doing and what I needed my diary and my notebook to do. In its idiosyncratic and unique way, I wanted to be able to:

- keep track of business and social appointments and events
- prioritize and schedule things to do
- keep a record of longer-term goals and intentions
- record ideas and help to bring them to fruition by making the time rather than hoping to find it
- and have all that in one handy place so I'd never again need to think 'now where did I put that ...?'

So here it is – *The Bullet-Point Life Planner* – the place to customize, organize and prioritize all your life admin into one convenient volume. Make it unique to your needs, feed it with information, and it will reward you endlessly.

- This is . . . .'s Bullet-Point Life Planner
- Dates covered. . . . .
- Address. . . . .
- Mobile. . . . .
- Landline . . . .
- Work phone. . . . .
- Email . . . .
- Skype username. . . . .
- Facebook username . . . .
- Instagram username. . . . .

INDEX

HOW THE BULLET-POINT LIFE PLANNER WORKS

Sometimes, the simplest ideas are the best. A straw, a roundabout, a funnel, they all do their job simply and elegantly with no need for fuss. That's what this planner is designed to achieve. So grab your planner and some coloured pens and we'll take a tour.

Everything you need in one place

• *The Bullet-Point Life Planner* is a practical tool designed to help you plan your life in a sensible and productive way. It is a blend of planner, diary, to-do list, Filofax, birthday calendar and all those odd notes on scraps of paper that end up crumpled in the bottom of your coat pocket.

• There are pages for every week of the year, plus quarterly and annual review pages.

• In addition, the thematic pages give you other options for recording information, from your career details to what you want to take on your next vacation.

• Bringing all these elements together means you never have to search round for the phone number of the guy who said he'd get you a discounted hotel, where you need to be for that meeting on Thursday or the name of your girlfriend's mum.

• At home and at work, you'll be sure never to miss an appointment, event or opportunity again.

You'll become the go-to person for up-to-the-minute information.

Make it a habit

• As some wise person once said, habits are harder to break than principles, so focus on making a habit of using your planner. All you need to do is keep your planner to hand and find the best place to fill in information as you acquire it. It will soon become second nature.

Index it

• To save you leafing through to find information, use the index pages at the front to jot down where to find specific notes so you can turn back to them easily and quickly.

Make it yours

• One key element of the planner is that while a lot of thought has gone into how it works and what it needs to include, it remains totally flexible and can be customized and personalized so that it fits exactly what you want it to be.

• If you want to change a heading, go for it. If you prefer to use an events page for a vacation, go ahead and use it.

Looking forward

• That keeps the present in check; what about the future? Having space to contemplate ideas, forward plan and meditate on your hopes and dreams can help you can begin to realize them.

• Find out other people's opinions too — it will help you in your decision making.

Looking back

• Finally, at the end of your year, you will have a complete journal — a snapshot of your year — to keep for future reference.

• Use the opportunity to make sure your life is progressing in the direction you want and think hard about filling in the most important lesson of the year.

Symbol selection

To encourage instant recognition of what needs doing, we have included a series of symbols to start you off — then you can add as many of your own as you like. To see how to create and personalize your own symbol selection, refer to page 11.

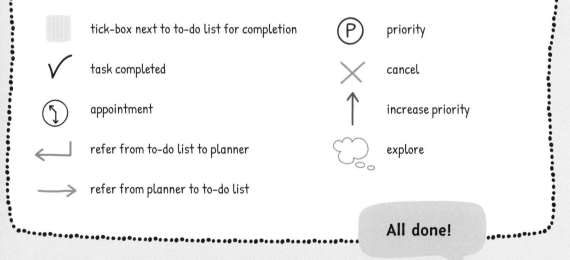

tick-box next to to-do list for completion

✓ task completed

↻ appointment

←⌐ refer from to-do list to planner

→ refer from planner to to-do list

Ⓟ priority

✕ cancel

↑ increase priority

explore

All done!

USING THE PLANNER FOR EVERY DAY

The Bullet-Point Life Planner is organized around weekly spreads, specially designed so that there is a place for everything – all you need to do is to put everything in its place. The weekly spreads start on page 20.

You can begin your planner whenever you like – there are enough spreads to take you through the whole year, whether that is 1 January to 31 December or 5 May to 4 May the following year – it's entirely up to you.

This is your planner, so use the sections as they were originally designed or adapt them creatively to suit your own needs. Keep it with you and fill things straight into the planner as they happen.

Dates and priorities

• So that you can start when you like during the year, make your first entries the week, month and year, then fill in the dates for that week.

• For most of us, a reminder of the things that absolutely must be completed will not go amiss. Fill in your priorities so that – even if nothing else happens – you can't say you forgot what was crucial.

Planner

• The planner gives you plenty of room to include the times and details of your appointments and events. Write down everything you need.

To-do list

• Of course, this leads on to the vital to-do list. There's room for you to list 12 things and that's deliberate because that's plenty for most people to fit into their busy weeks.

• Use arrows to target a particular time in your diary when you are going to get the jobs done. And use the tick-boxes to check them off when they have been completed.

Theme of the week

• As an added, thought-provoking idea, you'll find that each week has a space for a theme for the week.

• Get creative and think of a word, expression, phrase or style that really speaks to you and, ideally, is appropriate to what is going on during that week. You may like to ponder your theme when you are looking at your inspiration station, or perhaps use it to inspire your meal plans. Sometimes the themes will be useful just to get you thinking along new lines or to keep you focused on the bigger picture.

Event countdown

• If you are working towards an event that you have detailed on one of the information pages, use the event countdown to make sure your plans are going ahead in good time.

Meal plans

• We all try to keep to a healthy balanced diet – but it's not always easy. You might want to give yourself some encouragement by doing a little planning in advance so you know you are keeping to the right proportions and on track for a nutritious diet to keep you at a sensible weight.

Inspiration station

• This might be random thoughts that struck you as interesting; things you want to follow up but don't know when you'll have the time; fascinating words; pictures; fragments of poetry; music; doodles. Anything you like can go here.

Things I'm waiting for from other people

• There are often things we can't get on with because someone else in the chain is holding us up. They don't belong on our to-do list as we can't do them until it's our turn, but they must not be forgotten, so they go in this box.

• At the end of the week, these may need to be carried forward onto the next spread, along with any – hopefully few – other incomplete items.

Index it

• Don't forget to fill in the index pages at the front as you go along, so that you know where everything is and can find it again instantly.

• Write in your theme for the weeks and the dates, too.

Personalize your notes and symbols

It's up to you whether you use the symbols on page 9. If they resonate with you, great. If they look meaningless, just choose your own. The idea behind the symbols for the planner is that they:
• are quick and easy to use;
• are simple to draw;
• replace a relatively long piece of text;
• are instantly recognizable to you.
You may also want to use different colours for your marks and arrows to help you spot information, perhaps:
• red for important events;
• pencil for unconfirmed items;
• blue for dreams and distant things;
• green for go-ahead items.

PLANNING MAJOR EVENTS AND PROJECTS

When you are organizing a major event, there is a huge amount of crucial information that you need to keep to hand. You may well store a lot of it in your smartphone but what happens when you arrive at your destination and you've brought the wrong charger plug, or you get sand in your socket?

Adapt the planner to store all the essential information for easy access and back-up reassurance. The events spreads are on pages 34-5 and 98-9. The project spreads are on pages 66-7 and 138-9.

The event

• It could be a party, a wedding, a group of friends getting together for a weekend, a sports event or a fundraising bash. All these things take a lot of organization, so let our event pages help you make sure the occasion goes with a bang.

• If it is a major event, you may even want to use a couple of spreads to hold all your information, or an event spread and a data spread.

• Start with the date and time details, and the theme or style of the event to keep you focused.

The location

• Make sure you have the full details, including that all-important postcode.

• Sat navs can get confused in out-of-the-way places; check with the venue.

• What are the facilities?

Guest list

• Record the names and emails or contact details of the guests, ticked off when they have been invited, and marked whether or not they are going to attend.

Timeline

• A handy feature is a planning timeline, making it easier for you to keep abreast of your progress towards the big day.

• You'll also want to fill in the event countdown to keep on top of the planning and encourage the build-up of excitement.

Things to do

• A to-do list is at the heart of any planning project.

• You'll also need to plan the food and drink and decorations.

• When busy with the bigger picture, don't forget you're your own outfit. Does your suit need picking up from the cleaners? Do you need to schedule a shopping trip?

Projects

A similar spread can be used for projects that you are planning:

• decorating a room;

• de-cluttering your home;

• buying a car;

• starting up a new club or friendship group.

Simply apply the element headings to suit your project.

Remember to index it

GOING ON VACATION

Whether it's a short city break or a fortnight in the sun, a week in a remote castle or a full-on sightseeing tour, you'll need to do your planning if you want to get the most out of your vacation. Besides, if you put a lot into the planning and then the winding down, think how much better value the vacation is. You are getting all the pleasure you gain from those two weeks spread and magnified. The vacation spreads are on pages 44-5 and 82-3.

Firstly, jot down the dates, times and destination, with a few words to describe what you want out of the vacation: sun, sand and chilling, full-on sightseeing or cultural attractions, for example.

Language barriers

Why not aim to learn a little of the local language? It is polite to make an effort with the people you meet, even if you can only manage 'hello' and 'thank you'. Do check before you go, but here are a few general examples to get you started.

English	French	German	Spanish
hello	bonjour	guten tag	hola
goodbye	au revoir	auf wiedersein	adiós
please	s'il vous plaît	bitte	por favor
thank you	merci	danke	gracias

Arabic	Chinese	Swahili	
assalam alikum	ni hao	jambo jambo	
wadaeaan	zai jian	kwaheri	
raja	qing	tafadhali	
shukran	xiè xiè	asante	

Personalize it

The journey

• Every vacation starts when you set off out of the front door, and with a proper plan, you can allow plenty of time to have a relaxing journey and make the most of the time spent, rather than just seeing it as a means to an end.

• If you know you will have time on a train or in an airport, think about a couple of things you might shop for, take a book to read, puzzles, magazines – whatever you enjoy – or take the time to enjoy a meal at the airport or station.

• Will you need car hire? If you are taking your own car, are your insurance and breakdown cover suitable?

The destination

• Find out all you can in advance, study the web or a travel guide so you are well armed with information.

• What do you know about the resort?

• Are there particular places you want to see? Especially if they need to be pre-booked, check up on attractions or activities.

• Do you have recommendations for restaurants or attractions?

• What about special discounted tickets or multi-venue tickets?

• Jot down items to pack

The accommodation

• Make a note of all the contact details for your hotel or wherever you are staying.

• Find out about its facilities, restaurants, swimming pool, gym, parking, and so on. It would be a shame to turn up without a swimsuit if you have the opportunity to use the hotel pool, for example.

• Make sure you are aware of the check-in and check-out times.

Paperwork

• Note your passport number, details of your insurance policy and the emergency number, as well as your embassy or consulate contact details at your destination.

• Don't forget your budget. It is harder to go over budget if you have written it down.

• You may also need some local currency before you go and to check the facilities for using credit and debit cards. Check with your bank what charges they levy on your cards if you use them while you are abroad.

Index it

• Make sure you index all the planner spreads at the front of your planner.

USING THE INFORMATION PAGES

Interspersed through the weekly spreads are various pages for you to use to record information related to activities, events or specific goals. Choose the most appropriate page and personalize it to suit your needs precisely.

Annual calendar

• Use the calendar on pages 26-9 as an at-a-glance guide to birthdays, anniversaries and regular events.

• Fill in the year and month to start the calendar when you like, then add the event dates.

Career

• Use the career spread on pages 60-1 to keep your CV up to date by adding experience and skills as you acquire them.

• Define your ideal job and the skills you would need to get it. That will focus your mind on the practicalities of how to gain those qualities.

• Many of us are all too quick to self-criticize, so this is also where you big-up all the things you are best at.

Habits

• We have already noted that habits are harder to break than principles, so all the more reason to be aware of them and not just slip into them without thinking (see pages 76-7).

• It is often easier to spot the habits of other people than our own, so talk to someone you trust and listen to their opinion! Do you say 'like' or 'you know' too frequently? Do you interrupt? Fiddle with your cuffs? Twist strands of your hair?

• Make sure you are giving the most positive impression you can.

Achieving my objectives

• Link pages 108-9, if you like, with your hopes and dreams, but define a particular objective and look at the logistics of making it happen.

• You might want to lose weight, declutter the house, decorate a room.

• Define the steps you need to take, the potential benefits, who can help you achieve your aims, what stands in your way and how you aim to overcome such barriers.

Data records

• Usernames, telephone numbers, budgets – whatever you need an easily accessible note of can be contained on pages 116-7.

Brainstorming

• It does what it says in the heading on pages 132-3 – think about your main theme and group your creative ideas around it.

REVIEWING YOUR ENTRIES

Time flies past so quickly that it is easy just to get swept along, but the review pages give you a nudge to keep an eye on the bigger picture as well as the detail.

Hopes and dreams

• You might start on pages 18-19 with the one wish you would hold on to, or you might leave that until last.

• Distinguish between hopes — things that you know are within your capabilities — and dreams. In that column, think big. You may not make everything happen but it is good to have dreams.

• Decide on a mantra for the year: something positive that you can repeat when you feel you are not making progress.

• On the right-hand page, start to be a bit more practical. Specify concrete objectives with practical ideas on how you might achieve them and when.

• Look at your life at home, at work and out and about in your social sphere.

• Ask how other people view your plans, and set yourself some role models, people whose attitude and habits you can emulate.

Quarterly reviews

• When you get to the quarterly reviews on page 50-1, 82-3, 114-15 and 146-7, run through the previous three months and check that everything has been done that you were meant to do and, if not, to do something about it.

• It is also a good time to look at both what went right and what went wrong. We can often learn a lot from incidents that we could have handled better.

• Weigh up the work-life balance you have achieved — could it be improved?

• Even so, hanging on to regrets is no good to anyone, so think positive and record what you are most proud of through the previous three months.

• Having done that, try reviewing your hopes and dreams and looking forward to the next quarter of the year and how you are going to make the best of it.

• As well as general notes on what you would like to achieve, you might want to focus on specific areas of your life: home, work, social life, financial status.

Annual review

• The annual review on pages 158-9 takes a similar format except, of course, that you are looking at the whole year.

• Take your time over the annual review so that you make the best use of your progress through the year. Don't dwell on mistakes. Learn from them and move on.

Hopes and dreams

If I had one wish

....

....

Begin by distinguishing between hopes - things that you know are within your capabilities to achieve - and dreams. Decide on a mantra to help you direct your progress. Next you can set some practical objectives, think of inspiration you can take from people and situations in your life, and assess your concerns about what others may think. For more detailed instructions refer to page 17.

Hopes	Dreams

My mantra for the year: ....

....

To achieve my dreams, I need to:

_____

_____

_____

_____

_____

_____

Role models

_____

_____

_____

_____

SOCIAL LIFE

At home

....

....

....

....

....

....

....

At work

....

....

....

....

....

....

....

What other people think

....

....

....

....

....

....

....

Week

.... - ....

Month

....

Year

....

Priorities for the week

....

....

Planner

Date	Time	Appointments	Notes
MON			
TUE			
WED			
THU			
FRI			
SAT			
SUN			

Theme for the week is: ....

....

To do

- _____
- _____
- _____
- _____
- _____
- _____
- _____
- _____
- _____
- _____
- _____
- _____

INSPIRATION STATION

Meal plans

MON
....

TUES
....

WED
....

THURS
....

FRI
....

SAT
....

SUN
....

Things I'm waiting for from other people

Event countdown

....

weeks to

....

Week

-
............-............

Month

....

Year

....

Priorities for the week

....

....

Planner

Date	Time	Appointments	Notes
MON			
TUE			
WED			
THU			
FRI			
SAT			
SUN			

Theme for the week is: ....

....

To do

- _____
- _____
- _____
- _____
- _____
- _____
- _____
- _____
- _____
- _____
- _____
- _____

INSPIRATION STATION

Meal plans

MON
....

TUES
....

WED
....

THURS
....

FRI
....

SAT
....

SUN
....

Things I'm waiting for from other people

Event countdown

....

weeks to

....

Week
-
....
Month
....
Year
....

Priorities for the week
....
....

Planner

Date	Time	Appointments	Notes
MON			
TUE			
WED			
THU			
FRI			
SAT			
SUN			

Theme for the week is: ....
....

To do

- [ ] _____
- [ ] _____
- [ ] _____
- [ ] _____
- [ ] _____
- [ ] _____
- [ ] _____
- [ ] _____
- [ ] _____
- [ ] _____
- [ ] _____
- [ ] _____

INSPIRATION STATION

Meal plans

MON
....
TUES
....
WED
....
THURS
....
FRI
....
SAT
....
SUN
....

Things I'm waiting for from other people

Event countdown

....

weeks to

....

Annual calendar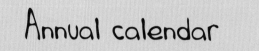

From ....
To ....

MONDAY	TUESDAY	WEDNESDAY	THURSDAY	FRIDAY	SATURDAY	SUNDAY

MONDAY	TUESDAY	WEDNESDAY	THURSDAY	FRIDAY	SATURDAY	SUNDAY

MONDAY	TUESDAY	WEDNESDAY	THURSDAY	FRIDAY	SATURDAY	SUNDAY

Fill in the year and month to start the calendar when you like, then add the dates to the individual monthly blocks. Include all your important events, birthdays and dates to remember.

 Birthdays   Anniversaries   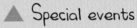 Special events

MONDAY	TUESDAY	WEDNESDAY	THURSDAY	FRIDAY	SATURDAY	SUNDAY

MONDAY	TUESDAY	WEDNESDAY	THURSDAY	FRIDAY	SATURDAY	SUNDAY

MONDAY	TUESDAY	WEDNESDAY	THURSDAY	FRIDAY	SATURDAY	SUNDAY

Annual calendar

From ....
To ....

MONDAY	TUESDAY	WEDNESDAY	THURSDAY	FRIDAY	SATURDAY	SUNDAY

MONDAY	TUESDAY	WEDNESDAY	THURSDAY	FRIDAY	SATURDAY	SUNDAY

MONDAY	TUESDAY	WEDNESDAY	THURSDAY	FRIDAY	SATURDAY	SUNDAY

Fill in the year and month to start the calendar when you like, then add the dates to the individual monthly blocks. Include all your important events, birthdays and dates to remember.

◇ Birthdays   ● Anniversaries   ▲ Special events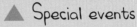

. . . .

MONDAY	TUESDAY	WEDNESDAY	THURSDAY	FRIDAY	SATURDAY	SUNDAY

. . . .

MONDAY	TUESDAY	WEDNESDAY	THURSDAY	FRIDAY	SATURDAY	SUNDAY

. . . .

MONDAY	TUESDAY	WEDNESDAY	THURSDAY	FRIDAY	SATURDAY	SUNDAY

Week

-

.... - ....

Month

....

Year

....

Priorities for the week

....

....

Planner

Date	Time	Appointments	Notes
MON			
TUE			
WED			
THU			
FRI			
SAT			
SUN			

Theme for the week is: ....

....

To do

- ☐ _____
- ☐ _____
- ☐ _____
- ☐ _____
- ☐ _____
- ☐ _____
- ☐ _____
- ☐ _____
- ☐ _____
- ☐ _____
- ☐ _____
- ☐ _____

INSPIRATION STATION

Meal plans

MON
....

TUES
....

WED
....

THURS
....

FRI
....

SAT
....

SUN
....

Things I'm waiting for from other people

Event countdown

....

weeks to

....

Week	Month	Year	Priorities for the week
.........-.........	....	....	....
			....

Planner

Date	Time	Appointments	Notes
MON			
TUE			
WED			
THU			
FRI			
SAT			
SUN			

Theme for the week is: ....

....

To do

_____

_____

_____

_____

_____

_____

_____

_____

_____

_____

_____

_____

INSPIRATION STATION

Meal plans

MON
....

TUES
....

WED
....

THURS
....

FRI
....

SAT
....

SUN
....

Things I'm waiting for from other people

Event countdown

....

weeks to

....

Week

.... - ....

Month

....

Year

....

Priorities for the week

....

....

Planner

Date	Time	Appointments	Notes
MON			
TUE			
WED			
THU			
FRI			
SAT			
SUN			

Theme for the week is: ....

....

To do

- _____
- _____
- _____
- _____
- _____
- _____
- _____
- _____
- _____
- _____
- _____
- _____

INSPIRATION STATION

Meal plans

MON
....

TUES
....

WED
....

THURS
....

FRI
....

SAT
....

SUN
....

Things I'm waiting
for from
other people

Event countdown

....

weeks to

....

Event

Date
...... : .... : ......

Time
.... : ....

Atmosphere
....

Guest list

Use this section to plan out a big event. Having all the details in one place will help you keep track of everything that needs to be done and make sure nothing is forgotten.

Name	Email	Invited	Accepted
....			
....			
....			
....			
....			
....			
....			

Timeline

-5 weeks	-4 weeks	-3 weeks	-2 weeks	-1 week	the day

To do

_____

_____

_____

_____

_____

_____

_____

_____

_____

_____

_____

COSTS

Venue details

....

....

....

....

....

....

....

Food and drink

....

....

....

....

....

....

....

Decorations

....

....

....

....

....

....

....

Week

.... - ....

Month

....

Year

....

Priorities for the week

....

....

Planner

Date	Time	Appointments	Notes
MON			
TUE			
WED			
THU			
FRI			
SAT			
SUN			

Theme for the week is: ....

....

To do

- _____
- _____
- _____
- _____
- _____
- _____
- _____
- _____
- _____
- _____
- _____

INSPIRATION STATION

Meal plans

MON
....

TUES
....

WED
....

THURS
....

FRI
....

SAT
....

SUN
....

Things I'm waiting for from other people

Event countdown

....

weeks to

....

Week
-
....

Month
....

Year
....

Priorities for the week
....
....

Planner

Date	Time	Appointments	Notes
MON			
TUE			
WED			
THU			
FRI			
SAT			
SUN			

Theme for the week is: ....
....

To do

_____

_____

_____

_____

_____

_____

_____

_____

_____

_____

_____

_____

INSPIRATION STATION

Meal plans

MON
....

TUES
....

WED
....

THURS
....

FRI
....

SAT
....

SUN
....

Things I'm waiting for from other people

Event countdown

....

weeks to

....

Week | Month | Year | Priorities for the week

........-......... | .... | .... | ....

....

Planner

Date	Time	Appointments	Notes
MON			
TUE			
WED			
THU			
FRI			
SAT			
SUN			

Theme for the week is: ....

....

To do

- _____
- _____
- _____
- _____
- _____
- _____
- _____
- _____
- _____
- _____
- _____
- _____

INSPIRATION STATION

Meal plans

MON
....

TUES
....

WED
....

THURS
....

FRI
....

SAT
....

SUN
....

Things I'm waiting for from other people

Event countdown

....

weeks to

....

Vacation

Dates

.... : .... : ....

.... : .... : ....

Style

....

....

....

Use this section to write down all the important details for your vacation plan.
Once you've done all the necessary planning, it will be easier to unwind and relax.

Travel

Destination

Accommodation

Check in: Check in:

Address ....   Address ....

....

Website ....   Website ....

Email ....   Email ....

Phone ....   Phone ....

To pack

_____
_____
_____
_____
_____
_____
_____
_____
_____
_____

To do

_____
_____
_____
_____
_____
_____
_____
_____
_____

COSTS

CURRENCY

Places to go

....
....
....
....
....
....
....

Recommendations

....
....
....
....
....
....
....

Emergency numbers

Travel

....

Accommodation

....

Insurance

....

Week

-
..........-..........

Month

....

Year

....

Priorities for the week

....

....

Planner

Date	Time	Appointments	Notes
MON			
TUE			
WED			
THU			
FRI			
SAT			
SUN			

Theme for the week is: ....

....

To do

- _____
- _____
- _____
- _____
- _____
- _____
- _____
- _____
- _____
- _____
- _____
- _____

INSPIRATION STATION

Meal plans

MON
....

TUES
....

WED
....

THURS
....

FRI
....

SAT
....

SUN
....

Things I'm waiting
for from
other people

Event countdown

....

weeks to

....

Week

-

....

Month

....

Year

....

Priorities for the week

....

....

Planner

Date	Time	Appointments	Notes
MON			
TUE			
WED			
THU			
FRI			
SAT			
SUN			

Theme for the week is: ....

....

To do

_____
_____
_____
_____
_____
_____
_____
_____
_____
_____
_____

INSPIRATION STATION

Meal plans

MON
....
TUES
....
WED
....
THURS
....
FRI
....
SAT
....
SUN
....

Things I'm waiting
for from
other people

Event countdown

....

weeks to

....

Week
-
...........-...........

Month
....

Year
....

Priorities for the week
....
....

Planner

Date	Time	Appointments	Notes
MON			
TUE			
WED			
THU			
FRI			
SAT			
SUN			

Theme for the week is: ....
....

To do

- _____
- _____
- _____
- _____
- _____
- _____
- _____
- _____
- _____
- _____
- _____
- _____

INSPIRATION STATION

Meal plans

MON
....

TUES
....

WED
....

THURS
....

FRI
....

SAT
....

SUN
....

Things I'm waiting for from other people

Event countdown

....

weeks to

....

Week | Month | Year | Priorities for the week

.... - .... | .... | .... | ....

....

Planner

Date	Time	Appointments	Notes
MON			
TUE			
WED			
THU			
FRI			
SAT			
SUN			

Theme for the week is: ....

....

To do

☐ _____

☐ _____

☐ _____

☐ _____

☐ _____

☐ _____

☐ _____

☐ _____

☐ _____

☐ _____

☐ _____

INSPIRATION STATION

Meal plans

MON
....

TUES
....

WED
....

THURS
....

FRI
....

SAT
....

SUN
....

Things I'm waiting
for from
other people

Event countdown

....

weeks to

....

Quarterly review

From

To

..... : ..... : .... : ..... : .....

I am most proud of
....
....

It's important to take some time out to review everything you've been working on. Every three months (or quarter of a year) is a good time to do this. Fill out these sections to track your progress.

Achievements	What I learnt
....	
....	
....	
....	
....	
....	
....	

Work-life balance assessment: ....
....

Looking forward

To achieve this	I need to

FINANCES

Good	Not so good

Work

Good	Not so good
....	....
....	....
....	....
....	....
....	....
....	....

Home and social life

Good	Not so good
....	....
....	....
....	....
....	....
....	....
....	....

Week	Month	Year	Priorities for the week
.... -	....	....	....
			....

Planner

Date	Time	Appointments	Notes
MON			
TUE			
WED			
THU			
FRI			
SAT			
SUN			

Theme for the week is: ....

....

To do

- _____
- _____
- _____
- _____
- _____
- _____
- _____
- _____
- _____
- _____
- _____
- _____

INSPIRATION STATION

Meal plans

MON
....

TUES
....

WED
....

THURS
....

FRI
....

SAT
....

SUN
....

Things I'm waiting for from other people

Event countdown

....

weeks to

....

Week
-
............-............

Month
....

Year
....

Priorities for the week
....
....

Planner

Date	Time	Appointments	Notes
MON			
TUE			
WED			
THU			
FRI			
SAT			
SUN			

Theme for the week is: ....
....

To do

☐ _____
☐ _____
☐ _____
☐ _____
☐ _____
☐ _____
☐ _____
☐ _____
☐ _____
☐ _____
☐ _____
☐ _____

INSPIRATION STATION

Meal plans

MON
....

TUES
....

WED
....

THURS
....

FRI
....

SAT
....

SUN
....

Things I'm waiting for from other people

Event countdown

....

weeks to

....

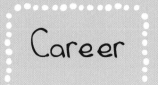

Career

Current job
....
....

Ideal job
....
....

Keep your CV up to date by adding experience and skills as you acquire them. Define your ideal job and the skills you would need to get it, in as much detail as possible. Focus on your strengths and how to accentuate your skills.

Ideal job specification

Skills required	How I match up
Qualifications required	How I match up

Weaknesses to be addressed: ....
....

Experience

_____

_____

_____

_____

_____

QUALIFICATIONS

_____

_____

_____

_____

Interests

....
....
....
....
....
....
....

Skills

....
....
....
....
....
....
....

Salary

....
....
....

Week
-
...........-...........

Month
....

Year
....

Priorities for the week
....
....

Planner

Date	Time	Appointments	Notes
MON			
TUE			
WED			
THU			
FRI			
SAT			
SUN			

Theme for the week is: ....
....

To do

- _____
- _____
- _____
- _____
- _____
- _____
- _____
- _____
- _____
- _____
- _____

INSPIRATION STATION

Meal plans

MON
....

TUES
....

WED
....

THURS
....

FRI
....

SAT
....

SUN
....

Things I'm waiting
for from
other people

Event countdown

....

weeks to

....

Week
-
..........-..........

Month
....

Year
....

Priorities for the week
....
....

Planner

Date	Time	Appointments	Notes
MON			
TUE			
WED			
THU			
FRI			
SAT			
SUN			

Theme for the week is: ....
....

To do

- _____
- _____
- _____
- _____
- _____
- _____
- _____
- _____
- _____
- _____
- _____
- _____

INSPIRATION STATION

Meal plans

MON
....

TUES
....

WED
....

THURS
....

FRI
....

SAT
....

SUN
....

Things I'm waiting for from other people

Event countdown

....

weeks to

....

Week

\-

..........-..........

Month

....

Year

....

Priorities for the week

....

....

Planner

Date	Time	Appointments	Notes
MON			
TUE			
WED			
THU			
FRI			
SAT			
SUN			

Theme for the week is: ....

....

To do

- [ ] _____
- [ ] _____
- [ ] _____
- [ ] _____
- [ ] _____
- [ ] _____
- [ ] _____
- [ ] _____
- [ ] _____
- [ ] _____
- [ ] _____

INSPIRATION STATION

Meal plans

MON
....

TUES
....

WED
....

THURS
....

FRI
....

SAT
....

SUN
....

Things I'm waiting
for from
other people

Event countdown

....

weeks to

....

Project

From	To	Description
...... : ...... :	...... : ...... :	....

Progress chart

Whether it's decorating a room, de-cluttering your home, buying a car or starting up a new project of any kind, there is usually a lot of crucial information that you need to keep to hand. Use this spread to record everything that needs doing.

....

....

....

....

....

....

....

Timeline

-5 weeks	-4 weeks	-3 weeks	-2 weeks	-1 week	the day

To do

- [ ] _____
- [ ] _____
- [ ] _____
- [ ] _____
- [ ] _____
- [ ] _____
- [ ] _____
- [ ] _____
- [ ] _____
- [ ] _____
- [ ] _____

COSTS

Ask for support from

....
....
....
....
....
....

Week
-
..........-..........

Month
....

Year
....

Priorities for the week

....

....

Planner

Date	Time	Appointments	Notes
MON			
TUE			
WED			
THU			
FRI			
SAT			
SUN			

Theme for the week is: ....

....

To do

- _____
- _____
- _____
- _____
- _____
- _____
- _____
- _____
- _____
- _____
- _____
- _____

INSPIRATION STATION

Meal plans

MON
....

TUES
....

WED
....

THURS
....

FRI
....

SAT
....

SUN
....

Things I'm waiting for from other people

Event countdown

....

weeks to

....

Week
-
..........-..........

Month
....

Year
....

Priorities for the week
....
....

Planner

Date	Time	Appointments	Notes
MON			
TUE			
WED			
THU			
FRI			
SAT			
SUN			

Theme for the week is: ....
....

To do

- _____
- _____
- _____
- _____
- _____
- _____
- _____
- _____
- _____
- _____
- _____
- _____

INSPIRATION STATION

Meal plans

MON
....
TUES
....
WED
....
THURS
....
FRI
....
SAT
....
SUN
....

Things I'm waiting for from other people

Event countdown

....

weeks to

....

Week

..........-..........

Month

....

Year

....

Priorities for the week

....

....

Planner

Date	Time	Appointments	Notes
MON			
TUE			
WED			
THU			
FRI			
SAT			
SUN			

Theme for the week is: ....

....

To do

- _____
- _____
- _____
- _____
- _____
- _____
- _____
- _____
- _____
- _____
- _____
- _____

INSPIRATION STATION

Meal plans

MON
....

TUES
....

WED
....

THURS
....

FRI
....

SAT
....

SUN
....

Things I'm waiting for from other people

Event countdown

....

weeks to

....

Habits

Best habit

....

Our habits are what make our character. What are the habits that you are happy with, and what are the ones you're not so happy with? This is a great exercise to help you take control over how you live your life and focus on cultivating the most positive version of yourself.

Good habits	Bad habits
....	....
....	....
....	....
....	....
....	....
....	....
....	....

Worst habit: ....

....

To encourage good practice

_____

_____

_____

_____

_____

To discourage bad practice

_____

_____

_____

_____

_____

Good habits I see in others

....

....

....

....

....

....

....

Bad habits I see in others

....

....

....

....

....

....

....

Week
-
....

Month
....

Year
....

Priorities for the week
....

....

Planner

Date	Time	Appointments	Notes
MON			
TUE			
WED			
THU			
FRI			
SAT			
SUN			

Theme for the week is: ....

....

To do

☐ _____

☐ _____

☐ _____

☐ _____

☐ _____

☐ _____

☐ _____

☐ _____

☐ _____

☐ _____

☐ _____

☐ _____

INSPIRATION STATION

Meal plans

MON
....

TUES
....

WED
....

THURS
....

FRI
....

SAT
....

SUN
....

Things I'm waiting
for from
other people

Event countdown

....

weeks to

....

Week

-

....

Month

....

Year

....

Priorities for the week

....

....

Planner

Date	Time	Appointments	Notes
MON			
TUE			
WED			
THU			
FRI			
SAT			
SUN			

Theme for the week is: ....

....

To do

☐ _____
☐ _____
☐ _____
☐ _____
☐ _____
☐ _____
☐ _____
☐ _____
☐ _____
☐ _____
☐ _____
☐ _____

INSPIRATION STATION

Meal plans

MON
....
TUES
....
WED
....
THURS
....
FRI
....
SAT
....
SUN
....

Things I'm waiting for from other people

Event countdown

....

weeks to

....

Vacation

Dates

.... : .... : ....

.... : .... : ....

Style

....

....

....

Use this section to write down all the important details for your vacation plan.
Once you've done all the necessary planning, it will be easier to unwind and relax.

Travel

Destination

Accommodation

Check in:

Address ....

....

Website ....

Email ....

Phone ....

Check in:

Address ....

....

Website ....

Email ....

Phone ....

To pack

_____
_____
_____
_____
_____
_____
_____
_____
_____
_____

To do

_____
_____
_____
_____
_____
_____
_____

COSTS

CURRENCY

Places to go

....
....
....
....
....
....
....

Recommendations

....
....
....
....
....
....
....

Emergency numbers

Travel

....

Accommodation

....

Insurance

....

Week

.........-.........

Month

....

Year

....

Priorities for the week

....

....

Planner

Date	Time	Appointments	Notes
MON			
TUE			
WED			
THU			
FRI			
SAT			
SUN			

Theme for the week is: ....

....

84

To do

- _____
- _____
- _____
- _____
- _____
- _____
- _____
- _____
- _____
- _____
- _____

INSPIRATION STATION

Meal plans

MON
....

TUES
....

WED
....

THURS
....

FRI
....

SAT
....

SUN
....

Things I'm waiting
for from
other people

Event countdown

....

weeks to

....

Week	Month	Year	Priorities for the week
..........-..........	....	....	....

Planner

Date	Time	Appointments	Notes
MON			
TUE			
WED			
THU			
FRI			
SAT			
SUN			

Theme for the week is: ....

....

To do

- _____
- _____
- _____
- _____
- _____
- _____
- _____
- _____
- _____
- _____
- _____
- _____

INSPIRATION STATION

Meal plans

MON
....

TUES
....

WED
....

THURS
....

FRI
....

SAT
....

SUN
....

Things I'm waiting for from other people

Event countdown

....

weeks to

....

Week	Month	Year	Priorities for the week
.........-.........	....	....	....
			....

Planner

Date	Time	Appointments	Notes
MON			
TUE			
WED			
THU			
FRI			
SAT			
SUN			

Theme for the week is: ....

....

To do

- _____
- _____
- _____
- _____
- _____
- _____
- _____
- _____
- _____
- _____
- _____
- _____

INSPIRATION STATION

Meal plans

MON
....

TUES
....

WED
....

THURS
....

FRI
....

SAT
....

SUN
....

Things I'm waiting for from other people

Event countdown

....

weeks to

....

Quarterly review

From .... : .... : ....

To .... : .... : ....

I am most proud of
....
....

It's important to take some time out to review everything you've been working on. Every three months (or quarter of a year) is a good time to do this. Fill out these sections to track your progress.

Achievements	What I learnt
....	
....	
....	
....	
....	
....	
....	

Work-life balance assessment: ....
....

Looking forward

To achieve this	I need to

FINANCES

Good	Not so good

Work

Good	Not so good
....	....
....	....
....	....
....	....
....	....
....	....

Home and social life

Good	Not so good
....	....
....	....
....	....
....	....
....	....
....	....

Week – ....-...........

Month ....

Year ....

Planner

Date	Time	Appointments	Notes
MON			
TUE			
WED			
THU			
FRI			
SAT			
SUN			

Theme for the week is: ....
....

To do

- _____
- _____
- _____
- _____
- _____
- _____
- _____
- _____
- _____
- _____
- _____
- _____

INSPIRATION STATION

Meal plans

MON
....

TUES
....

WED
....

THURS
....

FRI
....

SAT
....

SUN
....

Things I'm waiting for from other people

Event countdown

....

weeks to

....

Week

-

.... - ....

Month

....

Year

....

Priorities for the week

....

....

Planner

Date	Time	Appointments	Notes
MON			
TUE			
WED			
THU			
FRI			
SAT			
SUN			

Theme for the week is: ....

....

To do

- _____
- _____
- _____
- _____
- _____
- _____
- _____
- _____
- _____
- _____
- _____
- _____

INSPIRATION STATION

Meal plans

MON
....

TUES
....

WED
....

THURS
....

FRI
....

SAT
....

SUN
....

Things I'm waiting for from other people

Event countdown

....

weeks to

....

Week
-
..........-..........

Month
....

Year
....

Priorities for the week
....
....

Planner

Date	Time	Appointments	Notes
MON			
TUE			
WED			
THU			
FRI			
SAT			
SUN			

Theme for the week is: ....
....

To do

-
-
-
-
-
-
-
-
-
-
-

INSPIRATION STATION

Meal plans

MON
....
TUES
....
WED
....
THURS
....
FRI
....
SAT
....
SUN
....

Things I'm waiting
for from
other people

Event countdown

....
weeks to
....

Week	Month	Year	Priorities for the week

Week

·········· - ··········

Month

··········

Year

··········

Priorities for the week

··

··

Planner

Date	Time	Appointments	Notes
MON ····················			
TUE ····················			
WED ····················			
THU ····················			
FRI ····················			
SAT ····················			
SUN ····················			

Theme for the week is: ··

··

To do

- _____
- _____
- _____
- _____
- _____
- _____
- _____
- _____
- _____
- _____
- _____
- _____

INSPIRATION STATION

Meal plans

MON
....

TUES
....

WED
....

THURS
....

FRI
....

SAT
....

SUN
....

Things I'm waiting for from other people

Event countdown

....

weeks to

....

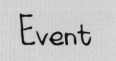

Event

Date	Time	Atmosphere
...... : ...... :	.... :	....

Guest list

Use this section to plan out a big event. Having all the details in one place will help you keep track of everything that needs to be done and make sure nothing is forgotten.

Name	Email	Invited	Accepted
....			
....			
....			
....			
....			
....			
....			

Timeline

-5 weeks	-4 weeks	-3 weeks	-2 weeks	-1 week	the day

To do

_____

_____

_____

_____

_____

_____

_____

_____

_____

_____

_____

COSTS

Food and drink

....

....

....

....

....

....

....

Decorations

....

....

....

....

....

....

....

What to wear

....

....

....

....

....

....

....

Week

............- ....

Month

....

Year

....

Priorities for the week

....

....

Planner

Date	Time	Appointments	Notes
MON			
TUE			
WED			
THU			
FRI			
SAT			
SUN			

Theme for the week is: ....

....

To do

- _____
- _____
- _____
- _____
- _____
- _____
- _____
- _____
- _____
- _____
- _____

Meal plans

MON
....
TUES
....
WED
....
THURS
....
FRI
....
SAT
....
SUN
....

Things I'm waiting for from other people

Event countdown

....

weeks to

....

Week

-

..........-..........

Month

....

Year

....

Priorities for the week

....

....

Planner

Date	Time	Appointments	Notes
MON			
TUE			
WED			
THU			
FRI			
SAT			
SUN			

Theme for the week is: ....

....

To do

_____

_____

_____

_____

_____

_____

_____

_____

_____

_____

_____

INSPIRATION STATION

Meal plans

MON
....

TUES
....

WED
....

THURS
....

FRI
....

SAT
....

SUN
....

Things I'm waiting for from other people

Event countdown

....

weeks to

....

Week

.... - ....

Month

....

Year

....

Priorities for the week

....

....

Planner

Date	Time	Appointments	Notes
MON			
TUE			
WED			
THU			
FRI			
SAT			
SUN			

Theme for the week is: ....

....

To do

- _____
- _____
- _____
- _____
- _____
- _____
- _____
- _____
- _____
- _____
- _____
- _____

INSPIRATION STATION

Meal plans

MON
....

TUES
....

WED
....

THURS
....

FRI
....

SAT
....

SUN
....

Things I'm waiting for from other people

Event countdown

....

weeks to

....

My objective

Steps to my goal

Details	Definition
....	....
....	....

Recalling what you wrote in your 'hopes and dreams' section, define a particular objective and look at the logistics and practicalities of making it happen. For more detail, see page 16.

Step	Detail	Timescale
....		
....		
....		
....		
....		
....		
....		

What will I gain if I achieve my objective? What will I forfeit if I don't?

....

....

....

....

To do

_____

_____

_____

_____

_____

_____

_____

_____

_____

_____

_____

PEOPLE WHO CAN HELP

What other people think

....

....

....

....

....

....

....

Barriers in the way

....

....

....

....

....

....

....

| Week | Month | Year | Priorities for the week |

Week
-
.... - ....

Month
....

Year
....

Priorities for the week
....
....

Planner

Date	Time	Appointments	Notes
MON			
TUE			
WED			
THU			
FRI			
SAT			
SUN			

Theme for the week is: ....
....

To do

- _____
- _____
- _____
- _____
- _____
- _____
- _____
- _____
- _____
- _____
- _____
- _____

INSPIRATION STATION

Meal plans

MON
....
TUES
....
WED
....
THURS
....
FRI
....
SAT
....
SUN
....

Things I'm waiting for from other people

Event countdown

....

weeks to

....

Week	Month	Year	Priorities for the week

Week
-
..........-..........

Month
....

Year
....

Priorities for the week
....
....

Planner

Date	Time	Appointments	Notes
MON			
TUE			
WED			
THU			
FRI			
SAT			
SUN			

Theme for the week is: ....
....

To do

- _____
- _____
- _____
- _____
- _____
- _____
- _____
- _____
- _____
- _____
- _____
- _____

INSPIRATION STATION

Meal plans

MON
....

TUES
....

WED
....

THURS
....

FRI
....

SAT
....

SUN
....

Things I'm waiting for from other people

Event countdown

....

weeks to

....

Week
..........-..........

Month
....

Year
....

Priorities for the week
....
....

Planner

Date	Time	Appointments	Notes
MON			
TUE			
WED			
THU			
FRI			
SAT			
SUN			

Theme for the week is: ....
....

To do

☐ _____

☐ _____

☐ _____

☐ _____

☐ _____

☐ _____

☐ _____

☐ _____

☐ _____

☐ _____

☐ _____

☐ _____

INSPIRATION STATION

Meal plans

MON
....

TUES
....

WED
....

THURS
....

FRI
....

SAT
....

SUN
....

Things I'm waiting
for from
other people

Event countdown

....

weeks to

....

Information back-up

In this digital age, we can often feel helpless without our smartphones or devices. Use this section to make a record of the important data that you would be lost without.

To do

☐ _____

☐ _____

☐ _____

☐ _____

☐ _____

☐ _____

Memberships

....

....

....

....

....

....

....

....

....

....

....

....

....

....

User names

....

....

....

....

....

....

....

....

....

....

....

....

....

....

Password clues

....

....

....

....

....

....

....

....

....

....

....

....

....

....

Week

-
..........-..........

Month

....

Year

....

Priorities for the week

....

....

Planner

Date	Time	Appointments	Notes
MON			
TUE			
WED			
THU			
FRI			
SAT			
SUN			

Theme for the week is: ....

....

To do

- _____
- _____
- _____
- _____
- _____
- _____
- _____
- _____
- _____
- _____
- _____
- _____

INSPIRATION STATION

Meal plans

MON
....

TUES
....

WED
....

THURS
....

FRI
....

SAT
....

SUN
....

Things I'm waiting for from other people

Event countdown

....

weeks to

....

Week
.... - ....

Month
....

Year
....

Priorities for the week
....
....

Planner

Date	Time	Appointments	Notes
MON			
TUE			
WED			
THU			
FRI			
SAT			
SUN			

Theme for the week is: ....
....

To do

_____

_____

_____

_____

_____

_____

_____

_____

_____

_____

_____

_____

INSPIRATION STATION

Meal plans

MON
....

TUES
....

WED
....

THURS
....

FRI
....

SAT
....

SUN
....

Things I'm waiting for from other people

Event countdown

....

weeks to

....

Week
...........-...........

Month
....

Year
....

Priorities for the week
....

....

Planner

Date	Time	Appointments	Notes
MON			
TUE			
WED			
THU			
FRI			
SAT			
SUN			

Theme for the week is: ....

....

To do

- _____
- _____
- _____
- _____
- _____
- _____
- _____
- _____
- _____
- _____
- _____
- _____

INSPIRATION STATION

Meal plans

MON
....

TUES
....

WED
....

THURS
....

FRI
....

SAT
....

SUN
....

Things I'm waiting
for from
other people

Event countdown

....

weeks to

....

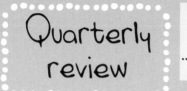

Quarterly review

From	To
...... : ...... :	...... : ...... : ......

I am most proud of
....
....

It's important to take some time out to review everything you've been working on. Every three months (or quarter of a year) is a good time to do this. Fill out these sections to track your progress.

Achievements	What I learnt
....	
....	
....	
....	
....	
....	
....	

Work-life balance assessment: ....
....

Looking forward

To achieve this	I need to

FINANCES

Good	Not so good

Work

Good	Not so good

Home and social life

Good	Not so good

Week
.... - ....

Month
....

Year
....

Priorities for the week
....
....

Planner

Date	Time	Appointments	Notes
MON			
TUE			
WED			
THU			
FRI			
SAT			
SUN			

Theme for the week is: ....
....

To do

- _____
- _____
- _____
- _____
- _____
- _____
- _____
- _____
- _____
- _____
- _____

INSPIRATION STATION

Meal plans

MON
....

TUES
....

WED
....

THURS
....

FRI
....

SAT
....

SUN
....

Things I'm waiting
for from
other people

Event countdown

....

weeks to

....

Week
-
....

Month
....

Year
....

Priorities for the week
....

....

Planner

Date	Time	Appointments	Notes
MON			
TUE			
WED			
THU			
FRI			
SAT			
SUN			

Theme for the week is: ....

....

To do

- _____
- _____
- _____
- _____
- _____
- _____
- _____
- _____
- _____
- _____
- _____

INSPIRATION STATION

Meal plans

MON
....

TUES
....

WED
....

THURS
....

FRI
....

SAT
....

SUN
....

Things I'm waiting for from other people

Event countdown

....

weeks to

....

Week
.... - ....

Month
....

Year
....

Priorities for the week
....
....

Planner

Date	Time	Appointments	Notes
MON			
TUE			
WED			
THU			
FRI			
SAT			
SUN			

Theme for the week is: ....
....

To do

_____

_____

_____

_____

_____

_____

_____

_____

_____

_____

_____

_____

INSPIRATION STATION

Meal plans

MON
....

TUES
....

WED
....

THURS
....

FRI
....

SAT
....

SUN
....

Things I'm waiting for from other people

Event countdown

....

weeks to

....

Brainstorming

Think about your chosen goal, a problem that needs solving or an idea that you want to expand on. Summarize it in the first box and then write down all the thoughts that flow from it. At the end, use the ideas on the page to draw your own conclusions.

Tip: Try not to spend too long thinking about what to write, just let the ideas flow in a 'stream of consciousness' style.

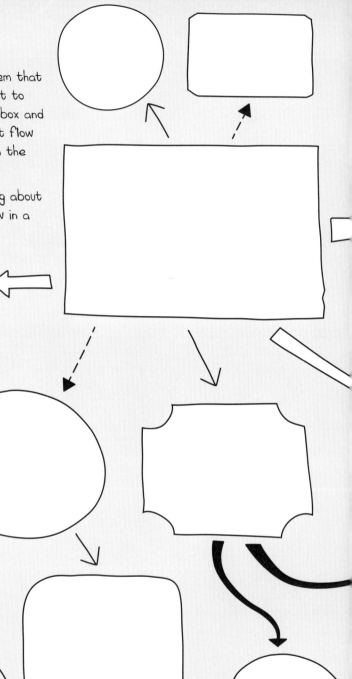

CONCLUSIONS

....

....

....

....

....

....

....

....

Week - ....

Month ....

Year ....

Priorities for the week
....
....

Planner

Date	Time	Appointments	Notes
MON			
TUE			
WED			
THU			
FRI			
SAT			
SUN			

Theme for the week is: ....
....

To do

- [ ]
- [ ]
- [ ]
- [ ]
- [ ]
- [ ]
- [ ]
- [ ]
- [ ]
- [ ]
- [ ]
- [ ]

INSPIRATION STATION

Meal plans

MON
....
TUES
....
WED
....
THURS
....
FRI
....
SAT
....
SUN
....

Things I'm waiting
for from
other people

Event countdown

....

weeks to

....

Week	Month	Year	Priorities for the week
.... -	....	....	....
			....

Planner

Date	Time	Appointments	Notes
MON			
TUE			
WED			
THU			
FRI			
SAT			
SUN			

Theme for the week is: ....

....

To do

- [ ] _____
- [ ] _____
- [ ] _____
- [ ] _____
- [ ] _____
- [ ] _____
- [ ] _____
- [ ] _____
- [ ] _____
- [ ] _____
- [ ] _____
- [ ] _____

INSPIRATION STATION

Meal plans

MON
....

TUES
....

WED
....

THURS
....

FRI
....

SAT
....

SUN
....

Things I'm waiting for from other people

Event countdown

....

weeks to

....

Week
..........-..........

Month
....

Year
....

Priorities for the week
....
....

Planner

Date	Time	Appointments	Notes
MON			
TUE			
WED			
THU			
FRI			
SAT			
SUN			

Theme for the week is: ....
....

To do

- ☐ _____
- ☐ _____
- ☐ _____
- ☐ _____
- ☐ _____
- ☐ _____
- ☐ _____
- ☐ _____
- ☐ _____
- ☐ _____
- ☐ _____

INSPIRATION STATION

Meal plans

MON
....

TUES
....

WED
....

THURS
....

FRI
....

SAT
....

SUN
....

Things I'm waiting for from other people

Event countdown

....

weeks to

....

Project

Progress chart

From	To	Description
...... : ...... :	...... : ...... :	....

Whether it's decorating a room, de-cluttering your home, buying a car or starting up a new project of any kind, there is usually a lot of crucial information that you need to keep to hand. Use this spread to record everything that needs doing.

....

....

....

....

....

....

....

Timeline

-5 weeks	-4 weeks	-3 weeks	-2 weeks	-1 week	the day

To do

☐
☐
☐
☐
☐
☐
☐
☐
☐
☐
☐

COSTS

Ask for support from

Week	Month	Year	Priorities for the week
........-........	....	....	....
			....

Planner

Date	Time	Appointments	Notes
MON			
TUE			
WED			
THU			
FRI			
SAT			
SUN			

Theme for the week is: ....

....

To do

_____
_____
_____
_____
_____
_____
_____
_____
_____
_____
_____

INSPIRATION STATION

Meal plans

MON
....
TUES
....
WED
....
THURS
....
FRI
....
SAT
....
SUN
....

Things I'm waiting for from other people

Event countdown

....

weeks to

....

Week

-
..........-..........

Month

....

Year

....

Priorities for the week

....

....

Planner

Date	Time	Appointments	Notes
MON			
TUE			
WED			
THU			
FRI			
SAT			
SUN			

Theme for the week is: ....

....

To do

- _____
- _____
- _____
- _____
- _____
- _____
- _____
- _____
- _____
- _____
- _____
- _____

INSPIRATION STATION

Meal plans

MON
....

TUES
....

WED
....

THURS
....

FRI
....

SAT
....

SUN
....

Things I'm waiting for from other people

Event countdown

....

weeks to

....

Week

-
....

Month
....

Year
....

Priorities for the week
....

....

Planner

Date	Time	Appointments	Notes
MON			
TUE			
WED			
THU			
FRI			
SAT			
SUN			

Theme for the week is: ....

....

To do

- _____
- _____
- _____
- _____
- _____
- _____
- _____
- _____
- _____
- _____
- _____
- _____

INSPIRATION STATION

Meal plans

MON
....
TUES
....
WED
....
THURS
....
FRI
....
SAT
....
SUN
....

Things I'm waiting for from other people

Event countdown

....

weeks to

....

Week

-

....

Month

....

Year

....

Priorities for the week

....

....

Planner

Date	Time	Appointments	Notes
MON			
TUE			
WED			
THU			
FRI			
SAT			
SUN			

Theme for the week is: ....

....

To do

- _____
- _____
- _____
- _____
- _____
- _____
- _____
- _____
- _____
- _____
- _____
- _____

INSPIRATION STATION

Meal plans

MON
....
TUES
....
WED
....
THURS
....
FRI
....
SAT
....
SUN
....

Things I'm waiting for from other people

Event countdown

....

weeks to

....

Week

-

....

Month

....

Year

....

Priorities for the week

....

....

Planner

Date	Time	Appointments	Notes
MON			
TUE			
WED			
THU			
FRI			
SAT			
SUN			

Theme for the week is: ....

....

To do

- _____
- _____
- _____
- _____
- _____
- _____
- _____
- _____
- _____
- _____
- _____
- _____

INSPIRATION STATION

Meal plans

MON
....

TUES
....

WED
....

THURS
....

FRI
....

SAT
....

SUN
....

Things I'm waiting
for from
other people

Event countdown

....

weeks to

....

Week
-
....

Month

....

Year

....

Priorities for the week

....

....

Planner

Date	Time	Appointments	Notes
MON			
TUE			
WED			
THU			
FRI			
SAT			
SUN			

Theme for the week is: ....

....

To do

- _____
- _____
- _____
- _____
- _____
- _____
- _____
- _____
- _____
- _____
- _____
- _____

INSPIRATION STATION

Meal plans

MON
....

TUES
....

WED
....

THURS
....

FRI
....

SAT
....

SUN
....

Things I'm waiting for from other people

Event countdown

....

weeks to

....

Week

..........-..........

Month

....

Year

....

Priorities for the week

....

....

Planner

Date	Time	Appointments	Notes
MON			
TUE			
WED			
THU			
FRI			
SAT			
SUN			

Theme for the week is: ....

....

To do

- _____
- _____
- _____
- _____
- _____
- _____
- _____
- _____
- _____
- _____
- _____

INSPIRATION STATION

Meal plans

MON
....

TUES
....

WED
....

THURS
....

FRI
....

SAT
....

SUN
....

Things I'm waiting for from other people

Event countdown

....

weeks to

....

Week

-
............-............

Month

....

Year

....

Priorities for the week

....

....

Planner

Date	Time	Appointments	Notes
MON			
TUE			
WED			
THU			
FRI			
SAT			
SUN			

Theme for the week is: ....

....

To do

- _____
- _____
- _____
- _____
- _____
- _____
- _____
- _____
- _____
- _____
- _____

INSPIRATION STATION

Meal plans

MON
....

TUES
....

WED
....

THURS
....

FRI
....

SAT
....

SUN
....

Things I'm waiting for from other people

Event countdown

....

weeks to

....

Annual review

From

...... : ...... : ......

To

...... : ...... : ......

I am most proud of
....
....

It's important to take some time out to review everything you've been working on. How has this year been for you?

Achievements	What I learnt
....	
....	
....	
....	
....	
....	
....	

Work-life balance assessment: ....

Looking forward

To achieve this	I need to

FINANCES

Good	Not so good

Work

Good	Not so good
....	....
....	....
....	....
....	....
....	....
....	....

Home and social life

Good	Not so good
....	....
....	....
....	....
....	....
....	....
....	....

MOVING ON

By the time you have been working with the planner for 12 months, you will hopefully be addicted and will be lining up a copy to take you through the next year.

- Jot down on this final page any information, events or objectives that you need to carry forward from one year to the next.
- Run through your inspiration stations and pick out things you particularly want to follow up.
- Make sure you are focusing on the positive as you turn from one year to the next.
- Here's to another great year!

Achievements

Carry forward to next year

The most important thing
I learnt this year is